So This is Me

So this is me...I'm a tad wacky and just shy of crazy.

And I love to create. Whether I'm painting fine art in my studio, drawing my wacky characters on location at shows, sitting at my pottery wheel on my back porch, or writing at my computer, the creative process is liberating beyond words. I am forever exploring new ways to express the energy inside me. But I feel forever blessed to have these gifts and vow to never take them for granted.

I'm 50-something years old and live mere feet from the ocean in a funky little surf town called New Smyrna Beach, Florida. Yes, I know. New Smyrna Beach has been officially declared the "Shark Bite Capital of the World," but the sand sparkles like white crystals and the water is a thousand shades of aqua blue. Waking up every morning to this glorious site makes my heart tingle. I share that space with my husband, Al, and a goofy Labrador retriever named Lucy. I eat chocolate truffles while I paint—and when they run out, I quit. I drink Perrier sparkling water so often I'm considering taking out stock in the company. I practice yoga, which for some strange reason I think will help compensate for my horrible diet, and I sit on the beach with my toes in the sand every chance I get.

I have five grown children and fourteen grandkids who love me as much as I adore them. I've taught them to dip their French fries in their chocolate shakes, make up any words they want to any tune they like, and to never, ever color inside the lines. (However, they all feel the need to assure their friends that they also have another set of grandparents who are "normal.")

Add the Color...
Feel the Tingle

There's nothing more satisfying than finishing a work of art. It adds excitement and joy to your life. Or to use my favorite tag line, you "Feel the Tingle."

The fact is, not everyone likes to draw, but everybody loves to color. Thus, anyone can experience the joy of participating in creating a piece of art with a coloring book. That's the genius of the medium. It's fun, interesting, and very fulfilling.

It doesn't matter how creative you are, you can learn about color and finish a masterpiece worth displaying. That's the purpose of this introduction—to teach you this skill.

If you already know this stuff, have a ball. If you don't, this information is way worth the effort. It will influence the way you color your entire world, from your home to your clothing to your food. Yes, even how you apply your makeup. And you will become a coloring book guru to boot.

So let's begin.

Color Selection Is Critical

You definitely want that "wow" factor when you're finished. So you need to know which colors do and do not complement each other. Do it right, and it will look like a Picasso.

The most essential tool in color selection is the color wheel, presented on the next page. Each color in the wheel is either PRIMARY, SECONDARY, or TERTIARY.

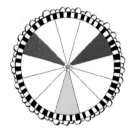

The primary colors are red, yellow, and blue. These are the root colors—they can't be created by mixing other colors. They are the pure foundation of the color wheel. All other colors are some combination of these three.

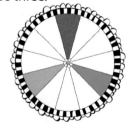

The secondary colors are orange, green, and purple. They are simply an equal mix of two primary colors (red + yellow = orange, yellow + blue = green, and blue + red = purple).

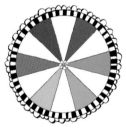

Tertiary colors are created by mixing a primary color with a secondary color. The resulting color is a matter of the percentage of the colors in the mix. There is no end to tertiary colors.

Colors are also categorized as warm or cool. Red, yellow, and orange are warm colors. Green, blue, and purple are cool colors. Selecting warm or cool colors really sets the mood of your piece. Warm colors are bold and exciting, while cool colors are more calm and peaceful.

Things really get interesting when you start playing with variations of a color. You can "tint" a color by adding white to the mix. Or you can "shade" a color by adding black.

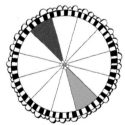

Colors opposite each other on the color wheel are called "complementary" and really pop off the page when they are used adjacent to each other. That's why you see yellow writing on purple backgrounds on billboards all over town. Or vice versa.

My Personal Twist

Since my earliest days as an artist, I have embraced the color yellow. Whether I am painting in my preferred medium of watercolors or dabbling in acrylics, pencils, markers, inks, or crayons, I almost always start with a layer of pale yellow—especially on a piece I want to be on the warm side of the color wheel. This assures that any work of art gets a wash of sunshine, whether the final colors are green, yellow, orange, or red. It really makes the colors pop. Greens get limey, oranges get a tangerine glow, reds get fiery, and yellows get even more electric.

And don't forget to leave open spaces with no color for white. It's easy to want to color every single nook and cranny with one of your fun colors, but leaving enough white is just as important to give your finished piece a lovely balance.

Celebrating the Sisterhood

It takes a lot of courage to grow up to be the wonderful wacky woman you were always meant to be

The Courage to Grow Up (mini), Color by Sarah Wilson
© Suzy Toronto • suzytoronto.com

Follow Your Heart (mini), Color by Sarah Wilson
© Suzy Toronto • suzytoronto.com

When You Stumble (Inspiration, mini), Color by Sarah Wilson
© Suzy Toronto • suzytoronto.com

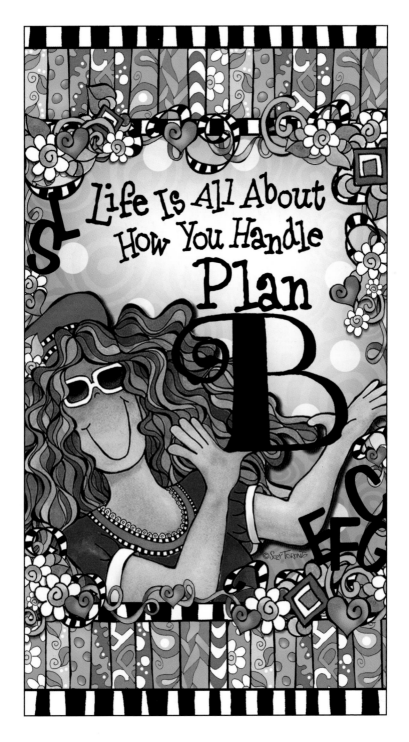

Plan B (Inspiration, mini), Color by Suzy Toronto
© Suzy Toronto • suzytoronto.com

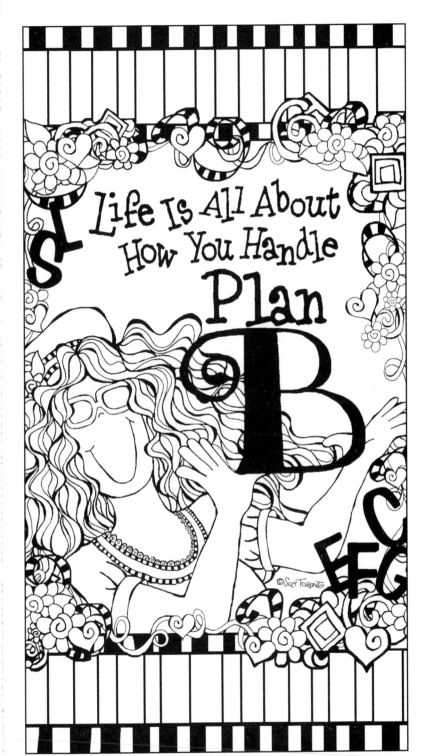

© Suzy Toronto • suzytoronto.com

Starting over is much harder than just starting. It's what builds character.

Plan B (Inspiration, mini)

I believe in you. I have always
believed in you. You are absolutely
over-the-top amazing...
don't ever forget it.

Crazy Brave & Wicked Strong (Inspiration, mini)

Be nice to everyone. You'll never regret being too nice.

A Hug Waiting to Happen (mini)

Be the change the world needs...
set a new standard and make a
difference whenever and
wherever you can.

Make Waves (mini)

If you only **pray** when you're in trouble... you're in **trouble!**

©Suzy Toronto

Take the time to breathe.
Learn to "do nothing" for a while.
You just might be really good at it.

_____
_____
_____
_____
_____
_____
_____
_____
_____
_____

Pray (mini)

Some of life's most profound lessons are learned at the most inconvenient times

© Suzy Toronto

Measure yourself by the depth
of your compassion, your thirst
for knowledge, and your
grace under fire.

_____

_____

_____

_____

_____

_____

_____

_____

Life's Lessons (mini)

If you want **rainbows**, you gotta have **rain.**

©Suzy Toronto

You never realize how high you
are without knowing how
low you've been.

Rainbows (mini)

Rise by Lifting Others

Heart Air
Balloon Rides
NO CHARGE

Make a difference in someone's life and in the process, you'll change your own.

Rise by Lifting Others (Inspiration, mini)

If you want something you've never had, you need to do something you've never done

©Suzy Toronto

Real living begins where your comfort zone ends. It is there you find the door labeled "Possibilities."

_____

_____

_____

_____

_____

_____

_____

_____

_____

_____

_____

Do Something You've Never Done (mini)

When you
Stumble
make it
part of the
Dance

There IS a "Do-Over" button.
It's labeled "Keep Trying."

When You Stumble (Inspiration, mini)

Take time...no, MAKE time
for yourself.

_____
_____
_____
_____
_____
_____
_____
_____
_____
_____

Make Each Day Ridiculously Amazing (mini)

When Life Gives You a Second Chance, **Take It!**

© Suzy Toronto

Color outside the lines. Life is too full of possibilities to conform to unimportant rules.

Second Chance (mini)

The cost of not following your **heart** is spending the rest of your life wishing you had

© Suzy Toronto

Make sure you are not
blocking your own light.

_____
_____
_____
_____
_____
_____
_____
_____
_____

Follow Your Heart (mini)

It takes a lot of courage to grow up to be the wonderful wacky woman you were always meant to be

©Suzy Toronto

The wacky light at the end of someone's tunnel could be you.

_____
_____
_____
_____
_____
_____
_____
_____
_____
_____

The Courage to Grow Up (mini)

Stop What You're Doing and Start Living

Breathe in the passion that
lights a fire in your soul.

Start Living (mini)

You can't start the next chapter of your life if you keep reading the last one

©Suzy Toronto

Your inner light may only be a flicker now, but it can be nourished and flourished. Once you find it, you will never be in the dark again.

Start the Next Chapter (mini)

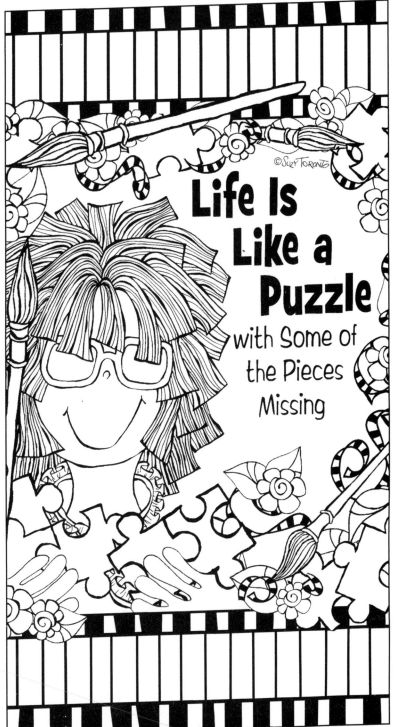

© Suzy Toronto • suzytoronto.com

In a world where bigger is better, sometimes you need to think small. Life is in the details.

Life Is Like a Puzzle

Ignite Your Passion

Fan the flames of what sets your heart on fire

© Suzy Toronto

Rekindle your passions and multiply your talents.

Ignite Your Passion (mini)

Don't call it a **Dream,**
Call it a Plan

©Suzy Toronto

Never say "the sky's the limit."
Live your life without boundaries.

_____
_____
_____
_____
_____
_____
_____
_____
_____
_____
_____

Call It a Plan (mini)

DON'T LET YOUR **FRAME OF MIND FRAME YOU IN**

You only see obstacles when you
take your eyes off your goal...
so FOCUS!

Your Frame of Mind (mini)

THERE ARE NO LIMITS TO THE **SILLY THINGS** I CAN ACCOMPLISH WHEN I AM SUPPOSED TO BE DOING **SOMETHING ELSE**

Permission Slip. (Good for a
day with no valid excuse.)

_____
_____
_____
_____
_____
_____
_____
_____
_____
_____
_____

Silly Things (mini)

You're wearing big-girl panties—
you can do anything.

Be Authentic (mini)

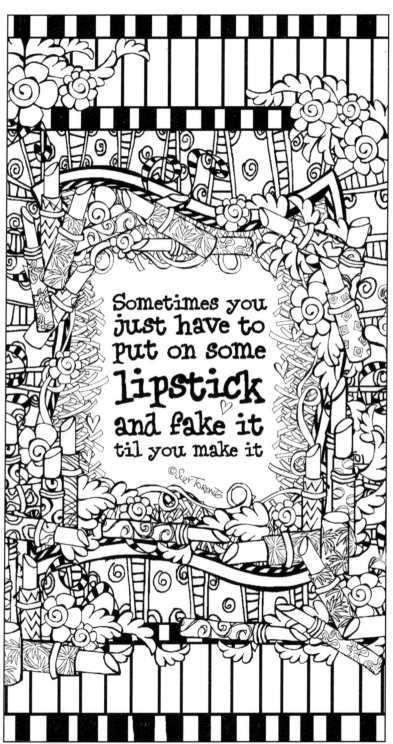

Sometimes you just have to put on some **lipstick** and fake it til you make it

© Suzy Toronto

Make yourself a milkshake.
It's hard to be unhappy when
you're drinking a milkshake.

_____
_____
_____
_____
_____
_____
_____
_____
_____
_____

Put on Some Lipstick (mini)

I am
Aware
that I am
Rare

©Suzy Toronto

Don't let anyone dull your sparkle.

I Am Rare (mini)

do not let
small minds
convince you
your dreams
are too big

©Suzy Toronto

Do not mistake your wild, unbridled
creativity for chaos and confusion.

Small Minds (mini)

When Life Becomes a
Roller Coaster,
Climb into the Front Seat,
Throw Your Arms
in the Air,
**& Enjoy
the Ride!**

Circumstances don't define us—it's
how we cope with them that does.

Enjoy the Ride (Inspiration, mini)

Don't let someone who gave up on their dreams talk you out of yours

©Suzy Toronto

If you're not willing to make a difference in this world, get out of my way.

Your Dreams (mini)

Learn to dream with your
eyes wide open.

Your Comfort Zone (mini)